The task was too important not to try something New.

Skeeples and Lomes
Published by Orange, a division of The reThink Group, Inc.
5870 Charlotte Lane, Suite 300
Cumming, GA 30040 U.S.A.

The Orange logo is a registered trademark of The reThink Group, Inc.

Other Orange products are available online and direct from the publisher.
Visit our website at www.WhatIsOrange.org for more resources similar to these.

ISBN: 978-0-9854116-7-1

Writer: Greg Payne
Illustrator: Brian Bascle
Art Direction: Ryan Boon

Printed in the United States of America
First Edition 2013

1 2 3 4 5 6 7 8 9 10

03/11/2013

SKEEPLES N LOMES!

by Greg Payne
illustrated by Brian Bascle

The Skeeples were yellow…

CRELUNKING TOOL

SILL-HAT

GIL-BOOTS

CRAVAT RESCUE ROPE

…no doubt about that!
From the points of their Gil-boots
to the lights on their Sill-hats,
but amazing Crelunkers when it came down to that
and they loved to help anyone stuck in a Cravat.

No matter how dark or how terrible the plight
the big yellow lamps on their Sill hats burned bright
illuming the corners with yellow spotlights.
They were born to do rescues and set things aright.

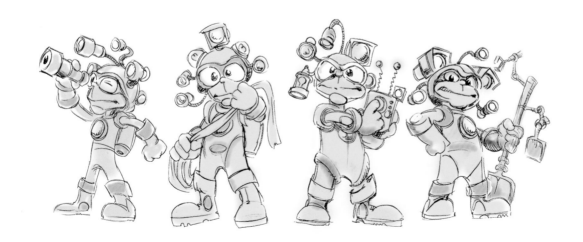

But the Skeeples were aloof,
often kept to themselves.
They lived up on Mount Tilley,
slept on yellow shelves.
They kept rescue equipment
for what'er befell.
They trained daily for rescues
and rang alarm bells.

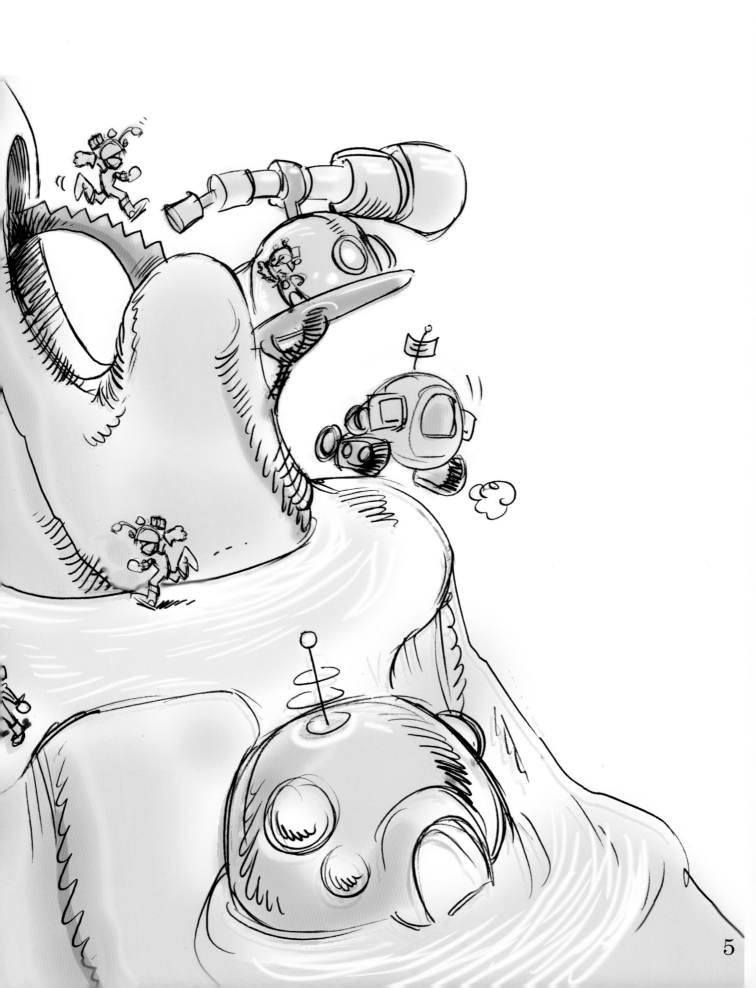

The Lomes were world famous as huggers and reachers.
At the foot of Mount Tilley they lived and they played. Sure,
the first thing you noticed when you saw these fine creatures
was their red colored bodies and red colored features.

The next thing you noticed if you were standing quite close
was a cozy tucked feeling, like warm buttered toast.
It made everything warmer, but they wouldn't boast
for this gift put inside them, inspired their utmost.

The Lomes all lived close at
the base of Mount Tilley.
The Skeeples on the mountain,
and the reason was silly.
They each got along, although
sometimes ill-will-y.
They'd lived close for years,
but relations were chilly.

Even so, that grand Mount was an idyllic spot.

Everyone was so thankful for the things that they'd got.

Both the Skeeples and Lomes would agree on this spot;

That they were most thankful for…

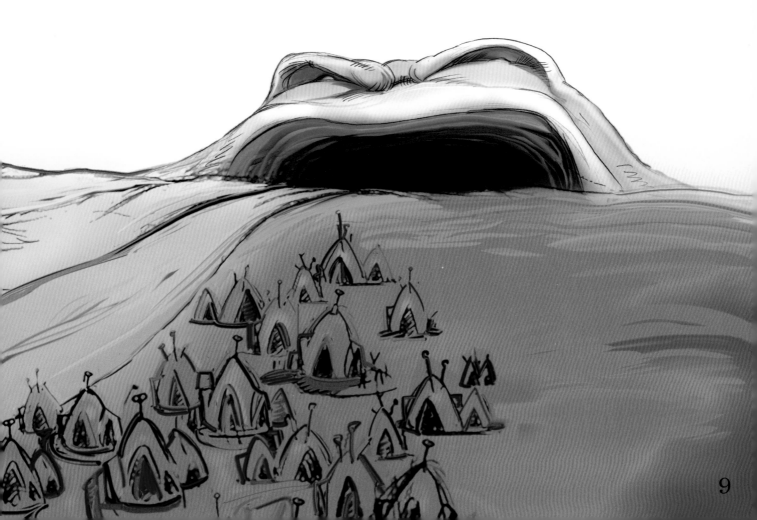

...the
Eph-lip-i-tots!

Eph-lip-i-tots were all cuddly and cute.

When they grinned or they giggled everyone "Awwwed,"

and said, "Shoot,

I love Eph-lip-i-tots. I love watching them grow.

I love their tiny red hands, and their wrinkly red toes."

11

Mostly, life on that mountain was exciting and fun.
The Lomes played in the shade. Skeeples warmed in the sun.
They'd say all of their problems boiled down to just one:
Eph-lip-i-tots tended to wander and run.

See, Eph-lip-i-tots were young. They had lots to learn.
To walk and to wander their tiny hearts yearned,
but often they'd tumble as teeny feet turned
toward the Cave of Cravats

...(and some didn't return).

I could tell a thousand stories of the 'tots and their beauty!
The most famous is about

Tinkit Potten

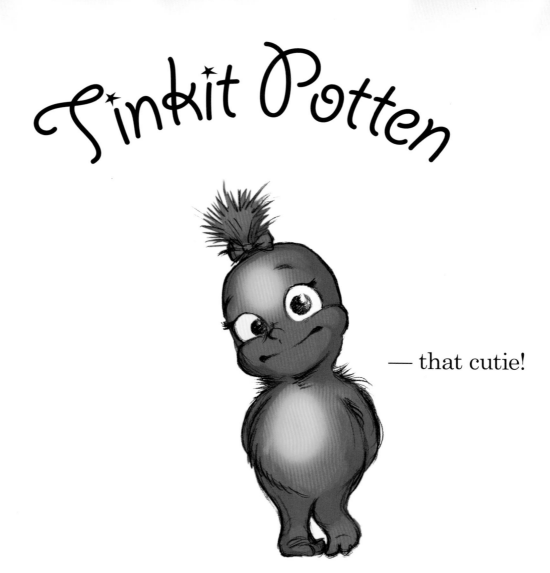

— that cutie!

She shared, and she sang, and she was never, ever snooty.
She was all charm, and all red, from her head to her booties.

Like every Eph-lip-i-tot she was made for a reason.
A treasure we hold, but just for a season.
To suggest any different would sound just like treason,
and this is one thing that red and yellow both agrees in.

So surprised were the Lomes the day Tinkit walked out
they mumbled, "She's walking toward the cave.
What's that about?"
At first they just whispered…

                              …then it turned to a shout,

"Tinkit Potten, come back!

              Please don't…

LOOK OUT!"

The Lomes fell behind crying,
"Please, Tinkit come back!"
but little Tinkit kept tottering
her dangerous track.

Then the Skeeple's bells rang,
and they loaded their packs.
"To the rescue!" they called
and ran down switchbacks.

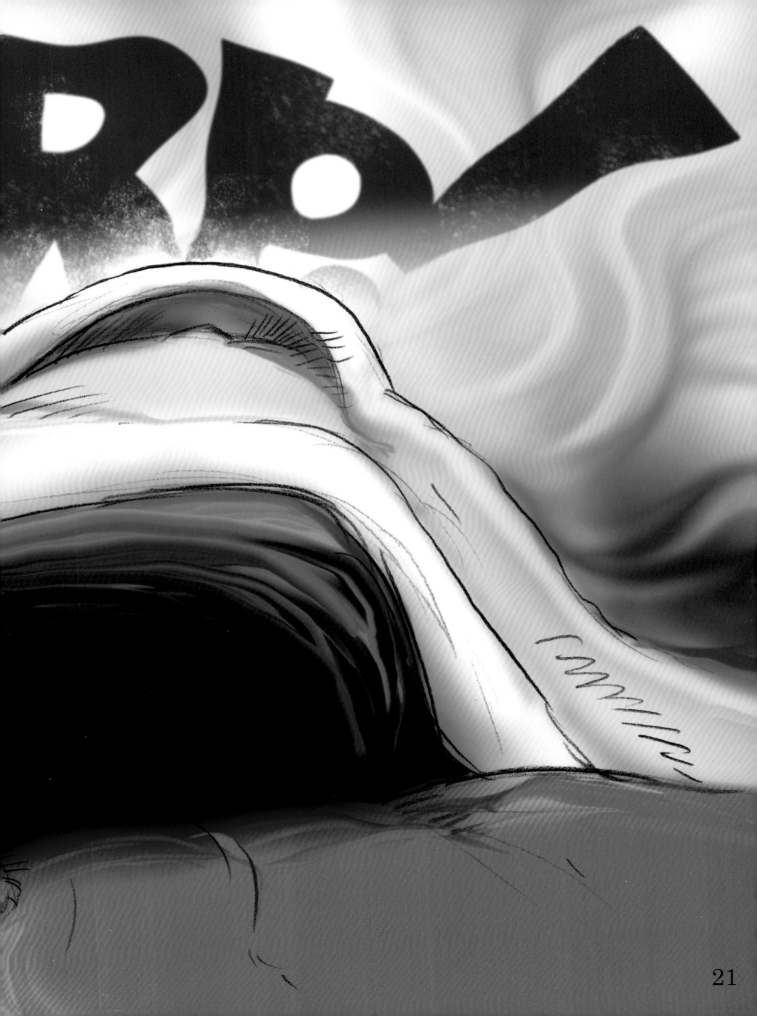

"GORP!" lurped the cravat as little Tinkit tumbled in
and turned her bright glow of red to a black gucky ruin.
As quick as a wink the glop grabbed to her skin.
(I wish she'd never found the evil cave with the goo in!)

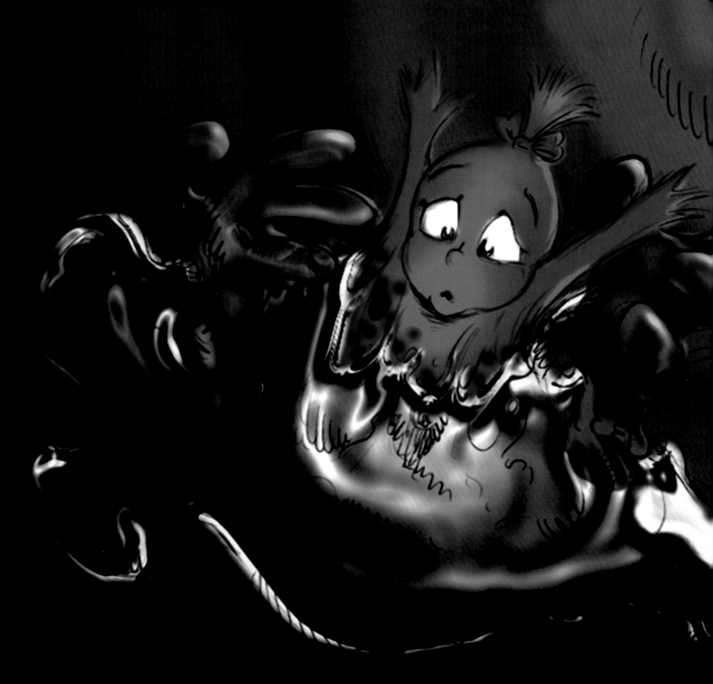

Then the two warmest Lomes
darted into the cave
headed straight toward poor Tinkit
(more determined than brave),
but it was so black and dark,
the situation was grave,
and they both thunk a thought,
"Can our Tinkit be saved?"

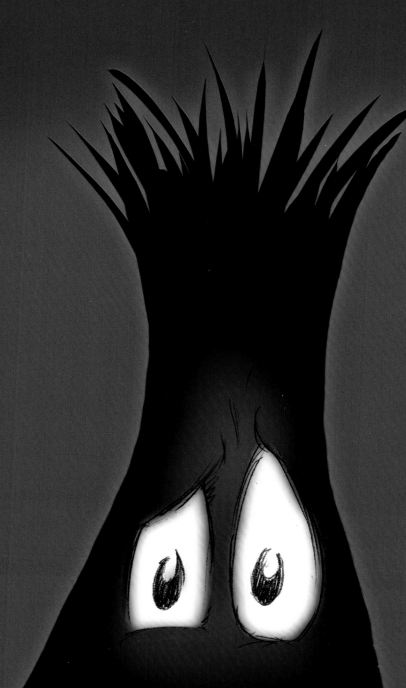

They planned to pull Tinkit all free from the harm
by filling the cave with the Lome's special warm
then the goo would get melty, release her red arms,
she'd get out of the pit and they'd end the alarms!

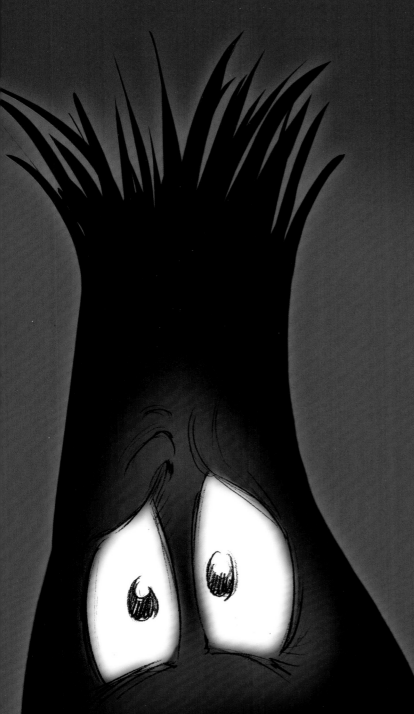

But the Lomes had a problem right from the start.

No matter how warm the love poured from their hearts,

they couldn't see Tinkit. The cave was too dark!

The two Lomes were forced from the cave to depart.

"We need some more help!" said a voice from the crowd.
And a heavy, dark silence came down like a cloud.
They all knew who to call, but now were they too proud?
Why, the Lomes call the Skeeples? It's hardly allowed.

The Lomes stood in silence outside the cravat.
They looked at their feet, and some held their red hats,
And right then, uninvited, a Crelunk rope went...

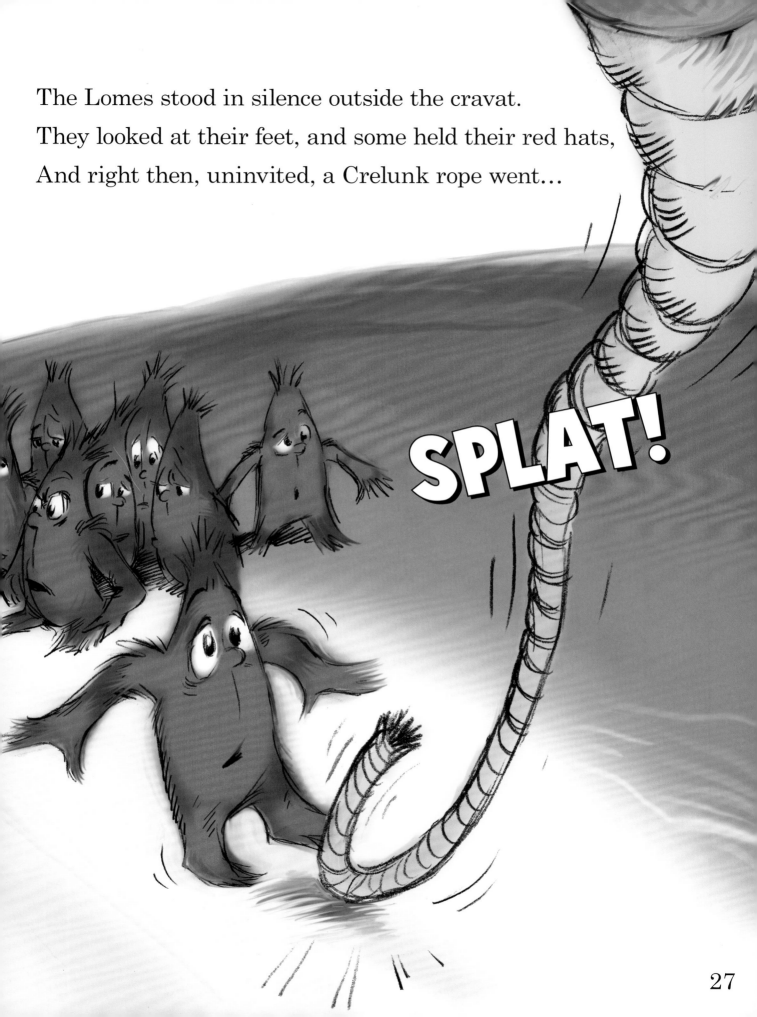

SPLAT!

And from over a rock, appeared a bright yellow hat.

Yes, the Skeeples came down from their Skeeply inclines
with their sill hats in place and all ready to shine.
They took charge and set up some bright yellow tapelines.
Finally, oh finally, things might work out fine!

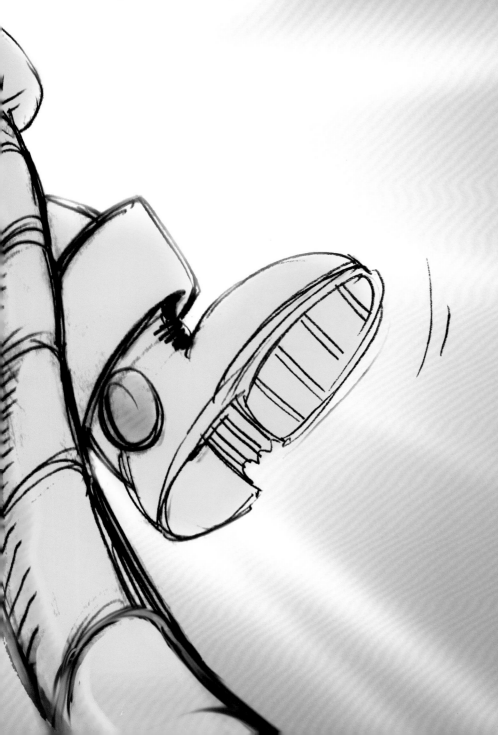

But one group of the Lomes just weren't ready for this.
"Just where have you been? You're too late!" they all hissed.
And some Skeeples were ready to cease and desist,
until they thought about the child stuck inside the abyss.

So the Skeeples kept working, although taken aback,
setting up lights without being sidetracked.
"Just leave it to us. Please, take one step back.
We'll get the child out. We've observed her whole track."

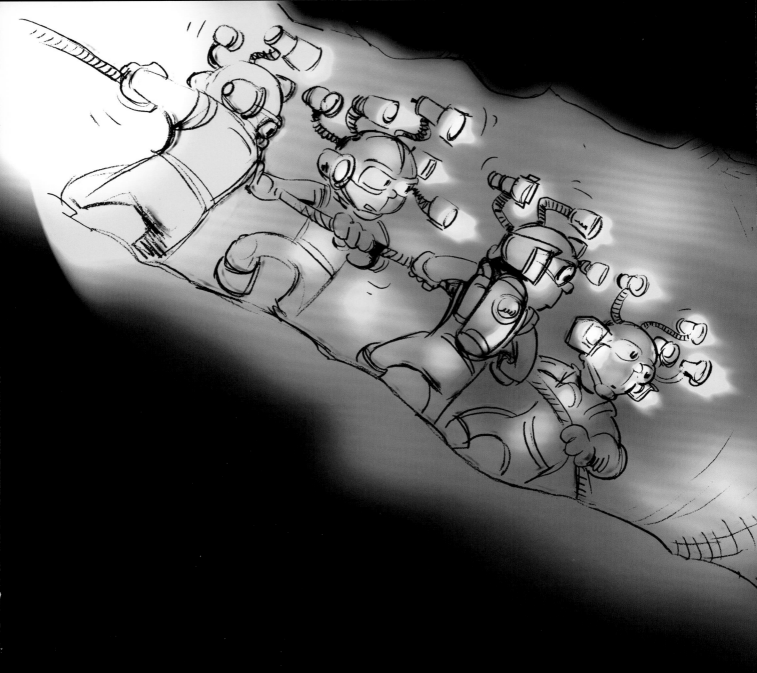

The Skeeples all worked with their confidence sure.

Their methods were proven, and their motives were pure.

All their lights lit the cave with no corner obscured.

In the dark cave they knew Tinkit couldn't endure.

Little Tinkit was stuck,
and that fact was plain…

34

…so the Skeeples mapped out the deadly terrain.

With the cave brightened up, they could see everything,

"We'll simply lift the child out, and success is attained!"

The rescue sounded so easy and quick,

'til they found that the goo was especially thick.

The red Lome child was caught in a cravat dirty trick

One Skeeple came out looking solemn,

sad,

and sick.

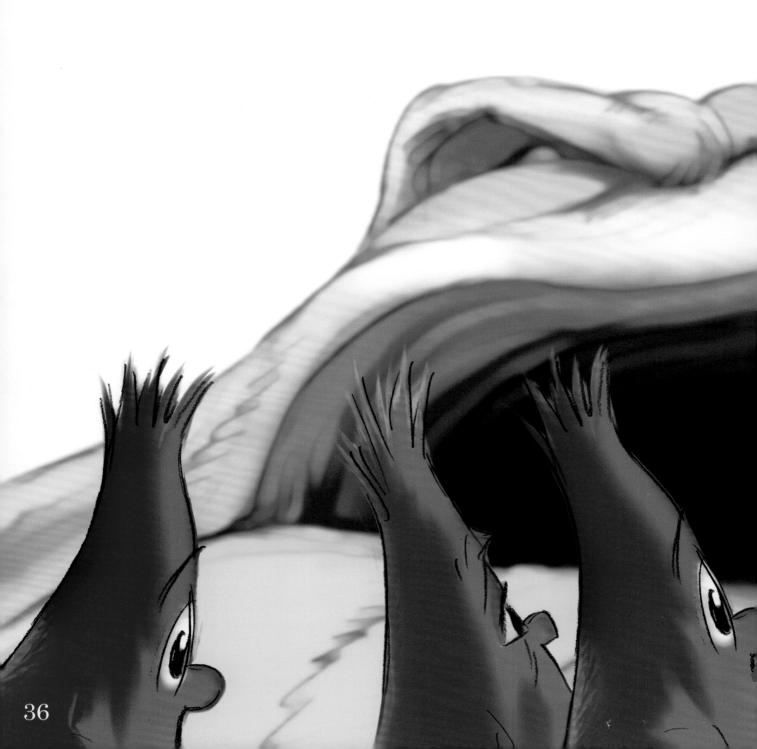

"We've assessed our assessment," he announced to the crowd.

"But it looks rather grim," he said not so loud.

"We can see that she's caught. She's stuck even now.

And we can't get her loose…

We just aren't sure how."

Some Lome's lips trembled. No one knew what to do.

Then through all the mumbled prayers,

one voice sounded through,

"But, well, what if we try it as one team, not two?

Let's all work together and get her out of that goo."

No one's sure who shouted, "But we can't do that!"
But a Skeeple looked away and then pulled down his hat.
"It's just not tradition," and he turned, and he spat.
"Mix red and mix yellow? Beside a *cravat?*"

Just then Grandpaw Lome spoke, "Now that's about enough!
I've heard red, and heard yellow, and all that old stuff.
We're going to save Tinkit. Don't give me no guff!
So, now who's on the team? Or do I have to get rough?"

And with that Grandpaw Lome marched his way right back in.

Then the quiet got thick, but pride started to thin.

Everyone stood still waiting 'til one Skeeple joined him.

Why, he followed the Lome, and by golly he grinned!

Red and yellow filled the cave,
coming in two by two.
The task was too important
not to try something new.
The Lomes warmed their hearts,
and their special heat grew,
while the Skeeples lit the cave up
like sunshine at noon.

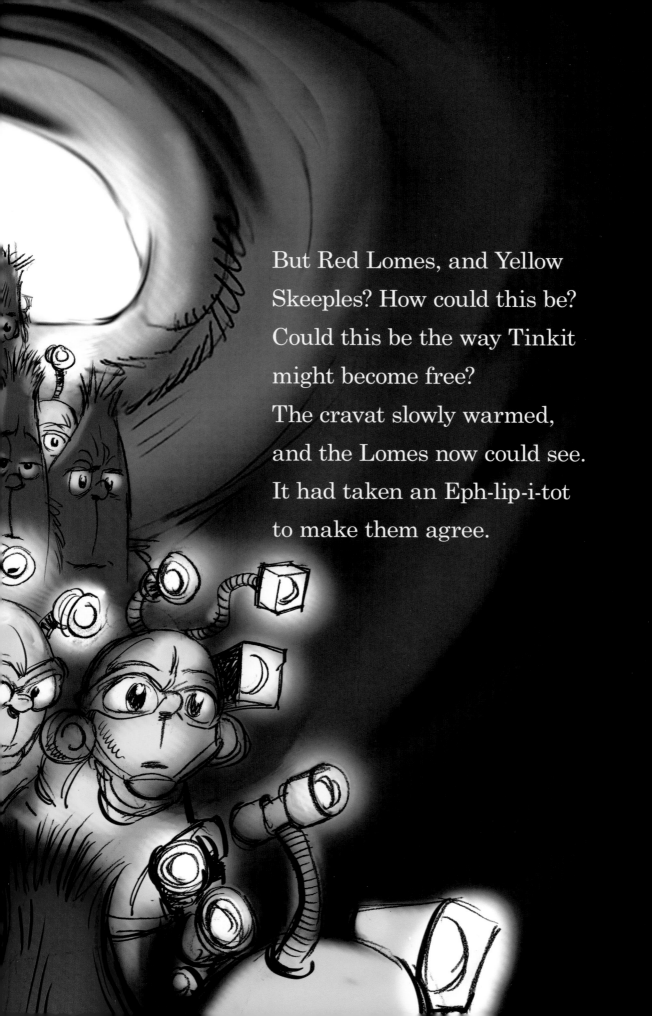

But Red Lomes, and Yellow
Skeeples? How could this be?
Could this be the way Tinkit
might become free?
The cravat slowly warmed,
and the Lomes now could see.
It had taken an Eph-lip-i-tot
to make them agree.

Then Grandpaw stepped up
and took Tinkit's red hand.

The Chief Skeeple stood by,
and then right on command…

45

The two pulled on her arms
and something wondrous began…

Tinkit's skin glowed
ORANGE…

…so bright,
and so grand!

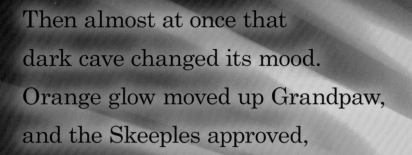

Then almost at once that
dark cave changed its mood.
Orange glow moved up Grandpaw,
and the Skeeples approved,

the Chief Skeeple glowed orange,
and all the Lomes "Oooooo'd!"
The cravat goo turned orange, and
Tinkit Potten...

...moved!

The orange Skeeple on one side, and Grandpaw on the other,
they lifted Tinkit out, and handed her to her mother.

50

As the tiny one was hugged until she nearly was smothered,
the orange glow spread to Aunts,
Cousins, and Brothers.

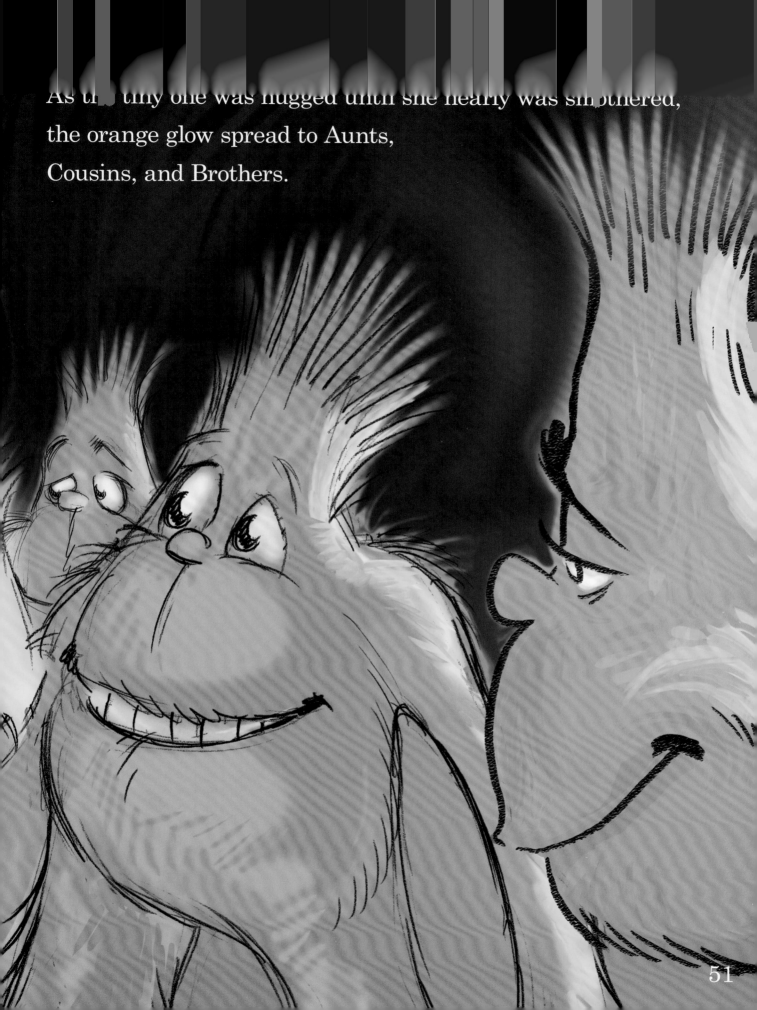

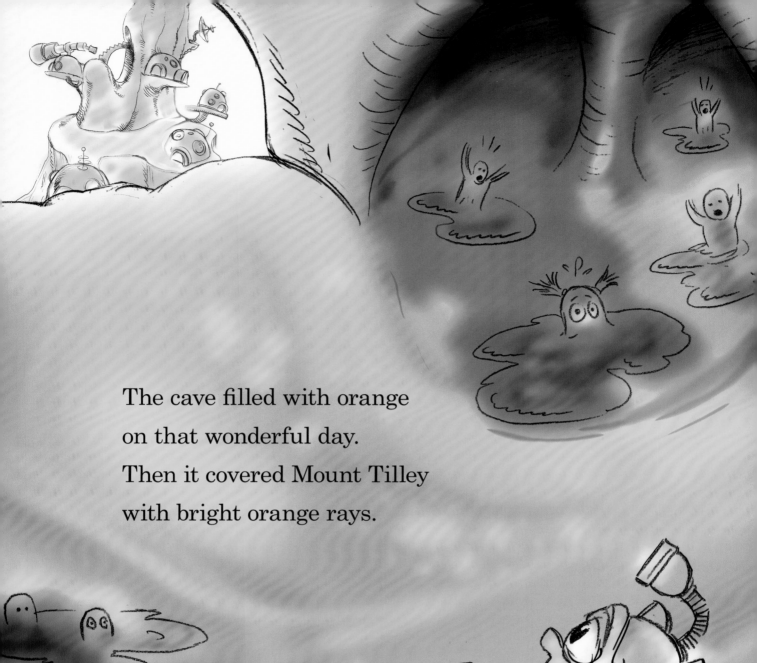

The cave filled with orange
on that wonderful day.
Then it covered Mount Tilley
with bright orange rays.

The Cravat Cave then brightened
it's other passageways
and more cravats were revealed
with 'tot's trapped and afraid.

53

Chief Skeeple then ordered, "Men, roll up your sleeves!"

And rescues began like you wouldn't believe.

Eph-lip-i-tots were unstuck and parents relieved.

It was a day that no Skeeple or Lome could conceive.

Just outside the cave's mouth
a party blossomed.
And as each 'tot was freed,
not a one went straight home.

They danced and they sang
under an orange Lome-dome,
had orange punch, orange cookies,
and orange ice-cream-foam.

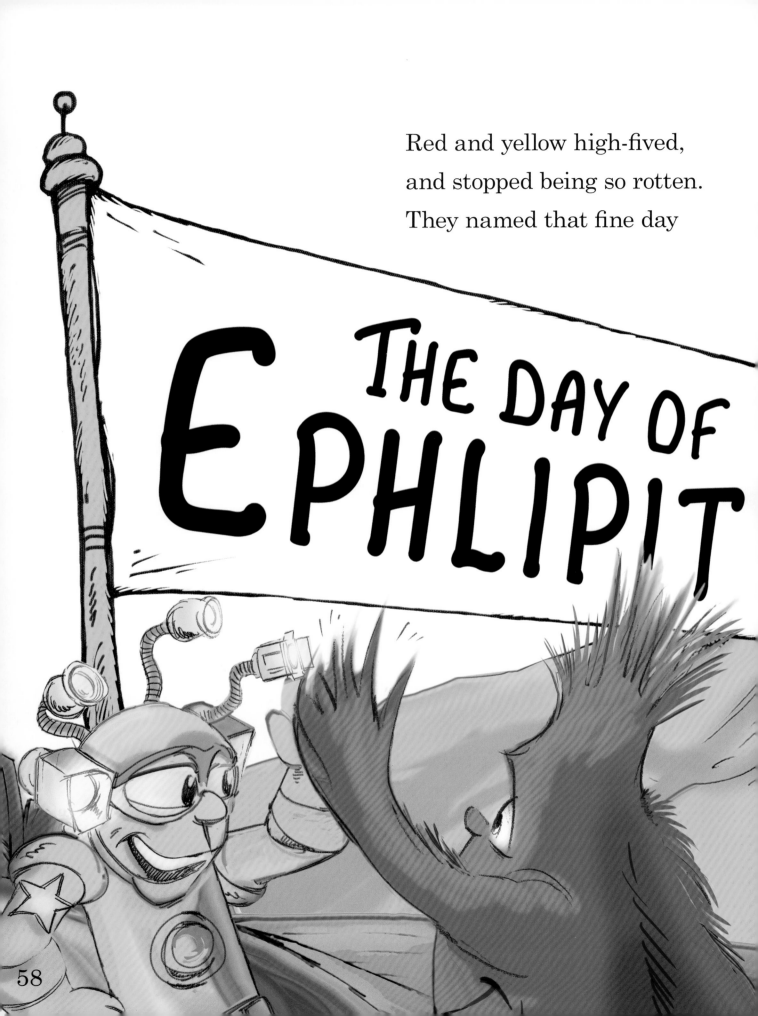

Red and yellow high-fived,
and stopped being so rotten.
They named that fine day

THE DAY OF EPHLIPIT

FREED
OT-EN!

The **Skeeples** and **Lomes**
were so glad that
they'd gotten
the importance of **Orange**.

59

Just ask

Tinkit Potten.

IF YOU ARE A SKEEPLE...

Thank you! Thank you for devoting part of your life, time, and talents to helping others. You don't do it for recognition, or thanks, or tangible gain. You do it because you *"were born to do rescues and set things aright."* You do the work that is messy and difficult because you care. You want to shine a light in some very dark places.

We hope you'll be able to use this story to remind yourself and others that the job is too important not to *"try something new."* That doesn't mean abandoning your purpose. It means that you know your job is so essential and so massive that you understand it's going to take all of us. It's going to take every one putting everything they have been given to work toward shining a light of truth and grace on a very dark world.

Orange is more than a color. It's a strategy. It means that you believe one plus one is greater than two. It means that you understand two **combined** influences make a greater impact than just two influences.

An Orange approach means that Skeeples have to ask themselves some questions. Are you doing everything you can to partner with the Lomes who need your help? Are you sweeping away as many obstacles as possible so you can work in a partnership with families? Are you setting up parents to succeed in their job as spiritual leaders in their homes?

If you'd like to meet more Skeeples who are asking the same questions and searching for ways to shine a light, go to **whatisorange.org.**

IF YOU ARE A LOME...

At some point, someone put a child into your arms and you have never been the same. You are so connected — heart, mind, and soul to another human being, that it's hard to imagine your life apart from them. Even if you didn't intend it, you have become an expert *"hugger and reacher."* Without a second thought, you walk through things that many people would avoid at any cost. You have an understanding of unconditional love that can only happen if you are a Lome.

We hope you enjoy this story as a way to remind you that you are never alone. Your job is not something anyone ever feels fully prepared to do. It doesn't have a day off. The most important moments are rarely planned. It unfolds a day at a time. One peanut butter and jelly, bruised knee, and muddy footprint on white carpet at a time. One step further as your Ephlipitot grows in wisdom, faith, and friendship.

Living as an Orange family means you understand that the job is bigger than just you. Other voices will become as important in your child's life as your own has been. You will face a time, or **many** times, when you will need someone to shine a light into your life — or your child's life — that will speak truth and grace in a way that it simply isn't possible for you to do.

The great news is that no matter where you are, no matter what you do, no matter what your circumstances, there are people who want to walk beside you. Skeeples. They don't want to do your job for you, but they do want to equip you, partner with you, and listen to you.

If you'd like to check out a community of people who have the same questions, struggles, and joys as you, go to **orangeparents.org.**

THE SKEEPLES AND LOMES VIDEO IS AVAILABLE FOR DOWNLOAD FROM THE ORANGESTORE.ORG

Acknowledgements

Greg Payne has been writing, working, eating, drinking, and thinking Orange since 1996. He and his wife Lynn enjoy watching their two Ephipitots grow in wisdom, faith, and friendship. He hopes that Carly and Greylin find very few cravats in their life (and thinly gooed ones at that!) and that their Orange Lome Dome parties are many.

Thank you to Reggie, and all the team at ReThink for investing their time and talents to help churches and families.

Brian Bascle is an artist, actor and voice talent. After reading this book it might surprise you to know that his favorite colors are green and blue, although he thinks red, yellow and particularly orange are pretty cool, too. He lives in Roswell, Georgia with his wife Jane, teen-lipitots Mike and Teresa, and two cats. There are rumors of a dog in the near future.